You're Our Kind Of Dog, Snoopy

Charles M. Schulz

Selected cartoons from
AND A WOODSTOCK IN A BIRCH TREE
Volume 1

CORONET BOOKS
Hodder Fawcett, London

Copyright© 1978 United Feature
Syndicate, Inc.

Reproduced by arrangement with
Fawcett Publications Inc., New York

Coronet edition 1982

British Library C.I.P.

Schulz, Charles M.
    You're our kind of dog, Snoopy.—(Coronet
books)
    1. American wit and humor, Pictorial
    I. Title
    741.5'973   PN6728.P4

    ISBN 0-340-28253-3

Printed and bound in Great Britain for Hodder
Fawcett Ltd., Mill Road, Dunton Green,
Sevenoaks, Kent (Editorial Office: 47
Bedford Square, London, WC1 3DP) by
Cox & Wyman Ltd, Reading

**Also by the same author,
and available in Coronet Books:**

ALL RIGHT, TROOPS... HERE'S WHERE WE CAMP FOR THE NIGHT

EACH SCOUT PITCHES HIS OWN TENT... AND THEN WE ALL GO TO SLEEP RIGHT AWAY...

JUST FOLLOW MY EXAMPLE

FOR OUR LAST NIGHT OUT I'VE PLANNED SOMETHING SPECIAL

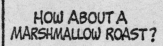

HOW ABOUT A MARSHMALLOW ROAST?

I'LL BUILD THE FIRE...YOU GET YOURSELVES SOME NICE LONG STICKS...

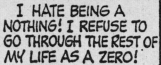

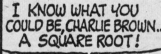

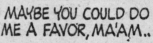

I will not fall asleep in class. I will not fall asleep in class.
I will not fall asleep
in class.
SCHULZ

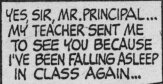

YES, SIR, MR. PRINCIPAL... MY TEACHER SENT ME TO SEE YOU BECAUSE I'VE BEEN FALLING ASLEEP IN CLASS AGAIN...

NO, SIR, I'M NOT BORED

AU CONTRAIRE!

JUST A LITTLE FRENCH THERE, SIR, TO KEEP YOU ON YOUR TOES...

A MOVIE, MA'AM?

THAT'S GREAT! I ALWAYS LIKE MOVIES

MOVIES IN THE CLASSROOM CAN BE ONE OF OUR BEST LEARNING TOOLS

Z

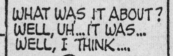

I'VE BEEN THINKING ABOUT YOUR PROBLEM, SIR

MAYBE YOU FALL ASLEEP IN CLASS BECAUSE OF UNCORRECTED ASTIGMATISM...

OH, SURE! YOU'D LOVE TO SEE ME WEARING GLASSES, WOULDN'T YOU, MARCIE?

SOME OF US THINK WE LOOK KIND OF CUTE WITH OUR GLASSES, SIR!

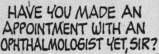

HAVE YOU MADE AN APPOINTMENT WITH AN OPHTHALMOLOGIST YET, SIR?

I DON'T WANT TO BE TOLD THAT I HAVE TO WEAR GLASSES, MARCIE!

YOU COULD BE SQUINTING AND NOT EVEN KNOW IT, SIR.. THAT CAN CAUSE EYE FATIGUE, AND MAKE YOU SLEEPY...

BESIDES, IF YOU WORE GLASSES, YOU MIGHT LOOK LIKE ELTON JOHN!

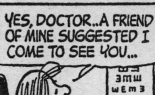

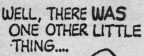

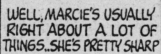

I CALLED HIM LAST NIGHT, MARCIE... I. CALLED CHUCK, AND I ASKED HIM IF HE LOVES ME...

THAT STUPID CHUCK!! HE DIDN'T EVEN KNOW WHAT TO SAY!

I THOUGHT TALKING TO HIM ON THE PHONE WOULD HELP...

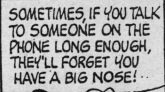

SOMETIMES, IF YOU TALK TO SOMEONE ON THE PHONE LONG ENOUGH, THEY'LL FORGET YOU HAVE A BIG NOSE!

SCHULZ

YOU SEE, SIR, WE ALL NEED SOMEONE TO KISS US GOODBYE...

NO ONE SHOULD BE EXPECTED TO GO OFF TO SCHOOL, OR TO WORK OR TO JOIN THE NAVY WITHOUT SOMEONE TO KISS HIM GOODBYE!

IT'S JUST HUMAN NATURE...

WE ALL NEED SOMEONE TO KISS US GOODBYE

"JOIN THE NAVY"?

LET'S JUST SIT HERE FOR AWHILE, AND ENJOY THE VIEW...

MAYBE WE'LL BE LUCKY, AND SEE A WHALE SWIM BY...

NO, OLIVIER, WHALES VERY SELDOM COME UP ON SHORE, AND ATTACK YOU

ALL RIGHT, LET'S SEE WHAT WE HAVE HERE FOR OUR EVENING MEAL..

I BROUGHT THE HOT DOGS...WOODSTOCK BROUGHT THE BUNS...

CONRAD BROUGHT THE MUSTARD...BILL BROUGHT THE CATSUP...

AND OLIVIER BROUGHT THE TV GUIDE!

SURPRISE!

I'VE BROUGHT YOU SOME AUTHENTIC BIRD'S-NEST SOUP!

AUTHENTIC? HOW DO I KNOW IT'S AUTHENTIC?

HEY, STUPID CAT! THAT WAS A NICE RAIN WE HAD LAST NIGHT WASN'T IT?

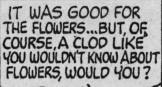

IT WAS GOOD FOR THE FLOWERS...BUT, OF COURSE, A CLOD LIKE YOU WOULDN'T KNOW ABOUT FLOWERS, WOULD YOU?

Sir Walter Scott's most famous novel was Ivanhohoho.

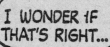

I WONDER IF THAT'S RIGHT...

YOU THINK MAYBE I SHOULD ADD ANOTHER "HO"?

THIS IS MY REPORT ON "OUR ANIMAL FRIENDS"

NOW, MANY OF YOU CITY KIDS ARE NOT ACQUAINTED WITH NATURE'S NOBLE CREATURES...

THEREFORE, AS A SPECIAL TREAT, I HAVE BROUGHT FOR YOU TODAY A REAL LIVE ANIMAL!

WHAT IS IT, A CHICKEN?

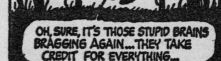

No.1
CRAB

SLAM!

BOY, DO I FEEL CRABBY!..

MAYBE I CAN BE OF HELP

WHY DON'T YOU JUST TAKE MY PLACE HERE IN FRONT OF THE TV WHILE I GO AND FIX YOU A NICE SNACK?

➤➤➤

SOMETIMES WE ALL NEED A LITTLE PAMPERING TO HELP US FEEL BETTER...

SEE? I CAME RIGHT BACK! HERE'S A NICE SANDWICH FOR YOU, SOME CHOCOLATE CHIP COOKIES AND A COLD GLASS OF MILK...

NOW, IS THERE ANYTHING ELSE I CAN GET YOU?

IS THERE ANYTHING I HAVEN'T THOUGHT OF?

YES, THERE'S ONE THING THAT YOU HAVEN'T THOUGHT OF.....

I DON'T WANNA FEEL BETTER!!

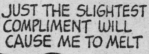

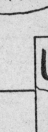

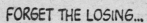

➤

HOW ABOUT THAT? I WALKED ALL THE WAY OUT HERE WITH YOUR SUPPER DISH BALANCED ON MY HEAD!

THIS IS WHAT HAPPENS WHEN YOU EAT IN THE SAME PLACE EVERY NIGHT!

LUCY, DEAR SISTER!

I ALMOST BOUGHT YOU A BIRTHDAY PRESENT JUST NOW

I SAW THIS BOTTLE OF COLOGNE IN A STORE WINDOW, AND IT ONLY COST A DOLLAR...

I KNEW IT WOULD MAKE YOU HAPPY TO GET IT, BUT THEN I SAW SOMETHING THAT I KNEW WOULD MAKE YOU EVEN MORE HAPPY!

IN THE WINDOW OF THE STORE NEXT DOOR, THERE WAS A SALAMI SANDWICH WHICH ALSO COST A DOLLAR...NOW, I KNOW HOW CONCERNED YOU ARE FOR THE PEOPLES OF THIS WORLD...

I KNOW HOW HAPPY IT'S GOING TO MAKE YOU WHEN I BECOME A FAMOUS DOCTOR, AND CAN HELP THE PEOPLE OF THE WORLD

BUT IF I'M GOING TO BECOME A DOCTOR, I'M GOING TO HAVE TO GET GOOD GRADES IN SCHOOL...

AND TO GET GOOD GRADES, I'M GOING TO HAVE TO STUDY, AND IN ORDER TO STUDY, I HAVE TO BE HEALTHY...

IN ORDER TO BE HEALTHY, I HAVE TO EAT...SO INSTEAD OF THE COLOGNE, I BOUGHT THE SANDWICH...ALL FOR YOUR HAPPINESS!

I'M SO HAPPY I COULD CRY!

'EEKS' ARE VERY IMPORTANT IF YOU'RE WRITING A STORY ABOUT A PRINCESS...

SAY THERE'S THIS BEAUTIFUL PRINCESS. WHO LIVES IN A CASTLE...SHE'S SITTING AT HER LOOM ONE DAY WHEN SUDDENLY A MOUSE RUNS ACROSS THE FLOOR...

"EEK!"

SHE CRIES...

IF YOU'RE DOING A STORY ABOUT A PRINCESS, YOU HAVE TO BE ABLE TO WRITE A GOOD 'EEK'

AN 'AWK' PROBABLY WOULD HAVE KILLED ME!

DO YOU REALIZE YOU JUST SLEPT THROUGH THE ENTIRE LESSON, SIR?

I DID? HOW EMBARRASSING!

AND WHEN YOU STARTED TO SNORE, EVERYBODY THOUGHT IT WAS A FIRE DRILL AND RAN OUTSIDE!

IT COULD HAVE HAPPENED, SIR!

"WRITE A THOUSAND-WORD ESSAY ON LOUIS XIV AND HIS ESTABLISHMENT OF THE ACADÉMIE ROYALE de DANSE"

"IDENTIFY REFERENCES AND SOURCE MATERIAL BY CHAPTER AND PAGE"

NO, MA'AM, I'M NOT SLEEPING...

I JUST PASSED OUT!

SCHULZ

I'M ALWAYS THINKING ABOUT THAT LITTLE RED-HAIRED GIRL, BUT I KNOW SHE DOESN'T THINK OF ME

SHE DOESN'T THINK OF ME BECAUSE I'M A NOTHING, AND YOU CAN'T THINK OF NOTHING!

YOU'RE NOT REALLY A NOTHING, CHARLIE BROWN

ALMOST

DOES A GIRL EVER GO AROUND THINKING OF A .00001 ?!

SCHULZ

YOU THINK YOU'D BE HAPPY IF YOU WON A BALL GAME, DON'T YOU, CHARLIE BROWN?

THE DOCTOR IS IN

WELL, YOU WOULDN'T! IF YOU WON ONE GAME, YOU'D WANT TO WIN ANOTHER, AND THEN ANOTHER!

SOON YOU'D WANT TO WIN EVERY BALL GAME YOU PLAYED...

YEAHHH!!

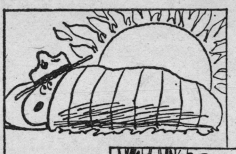

MORE PEANUTS TITLES FROM CORONET

CHARLES M. SCHULZ

☐ 24270 1	You've Got To Be Kidding Snoopy (54)	75p
☐ 24517 4	It's Show Time Snoopy (55)	75p
☐ 24499 2	Snoopy And The Red Baron (Colour)	75p
☐ 24875 0	Keep Up The Good Work Charlie Brown (56)	75p
☐ 25398 3	It's Raining On Your Parade Charlie Brown (57)	65p
☐ 25478 5	Think Thinner Snoopy (58)	75p
☐ 25865 9	Let's Hear It For Dinner Snoopy (59)	75p
☐ 26467 5	Think About It Tomorrow Snoopy (60)	75p
☐ 26667 8	Jogging Is In Snoopy (61)	75p
☐ 26801 8	Love And Kisses (62)	75p
☐ 27265 1	Stay With It Snoopy (63)	75p
☐ 27861 7	Snoopy Top Dog (64)	85p

All these books are available at your local bookshop or newsagent, or can be ordered direct from the publisher. Just tick the titles you want and fill in the form below.

Prices and availability subject to change without notice.

CORONET BOOKS, P.O. Box 11, Falmouth, Cornwall.

Please send cheque or postal order, and allow the following for postage and packing:

U.K. – 40p for one book, plus 18p for the second book, and 13p for each additional book ordered up to a £1.49 maximum.

B.F.P.O. and EIRE – 40p for the first book, plus 18p for the second book, and 13p per copy for the next 7 books, 7p per book thereafter.

OTHER OVERSEAS CUSTOMERS – 60p for the first book, plus 18p per copy for each additional book.

Name ....

Address..

....